TROMBONE / EUPHONIUM (Bass clef)

TEAM BRASS

RICHARD DUCKETT

The author is donating a percentage of his royalties from Team Brass
To the Save The Children Fund

International Music Publications Limited

Introduction

The TEAM BRASS series has been designed to meet the needs of young brass musicians everywhere, whether lessons are given individually, in groups or in the classroom.

Musical variety

Each book contains a wide range of musical styles, from the Baroque and Classical eras to film, folk, jazz and latin American. In addition there are original pieces and studies, technical exercises and scales, progressing from the beginner stage to approximately Grade IV standard of the *Associated Board of the Royal Schools of Music*. Furthermore TEAM BRASS offers material suitable for mixed brass ensemble as well as solos with piano accompaniment.

Ensemble pieces

All TEAM BRASS books contain corresponding pages of music which can be played together in harmony. Beginners are thus given early ensemble experience and the opportunity to share sessions with other players, be they treble or bass clef, B flat, E flat or F pitched instruments, and occasionally with guitar or synthesizer.

Study options

The TEAM BRASS series is not a "method". It is a collection of primer music from which the teacher can select a suitably graded course for each pupil. This allows for variation in starting-point, concentration threshold and tempo of progression. There is in TEAM BRASS a choice of starting-notes and several choices of progressive path the pupil can follow. Study options appear at the foot of most pages.

The terms *crotchet, quaver, minim etc.*, are used throughout this series instead of *quarter-note, eighth-note, half-note etc.* It is felt that, as pupils will probably need to know both systems, the less easily remembered terms should be learned first — one at a time. Later there will be no difficulty in learning the alternative, more logically-based fraction names.

This series is ideal for use with the upper primary and lower secondary age-range.

G.C.S.E. skills

In addition to fostering musical literacy, *Rhythm Grids, Letter-name Grids,* and *Play By Ear* lines provide early opportunities for composition and improvisation. This aspect of TEAM BRASS can be a useful starting-point for these elements in the GCSE Examination course now followed in many secondary schools.

Comprehensive notes on the use of this series, scores of ensemble pieces, piano accompaniments and approaches to creative music-making are given in the *Accompaniments Book*.

Team Brass Ensemble

TEAM BRASS ensemble material has been specially written so that it can be played by almost any combination of brass instruments that the teacher is likely to encounter. The pieces are basically for duet, to which can be added independent (and inessential) third and fourth parts if required.

This book contains thirteen trombone duets. Related third and fourth parts to these appear in the *F Horn book* and in the *Supplement to the Brass Band book*. In addition, a trombone trio can be achieved by combining the duet arrangement with the *'Bass part with trumpet duet'* appearing on the same page.

In all cases, combined material appears on the same numbered pages in the books concerned. For example, on page 14 will be found *German Dance* as a duet and also a bass part to accompany the duet found on page 14 of the *Trumpet* and *Brass Band* books. Also to be found are lower parts for adding to the duets in the *F Horn book*.

All the ensemble pieces are graded to match the lesson material. These may be easily located by following the direction at the foot of the appropriate lesson page. Scores for all ensemble material and more extensive notes appear in the *Accompaniments Book*.

The following symbols have been used to provide an immediate visual identification:

 Pieces with Piano Accompaniment

 Part of an Ensemble arrangement
(score included in *Accompaniments Book*)

Because the ensemble pieces provide a meeting point for players who are at various stages of development, these may include technical elements (new notes, rhythms etc.,) which are not in fact introduced until some pages later.

For MARY

Edited by WILLIAM RUMFORD Instrumental Organiser
for the London Borough of Brent
PHILIP EVRY and GEOFFRY RUSSELL-SMITH

Piano accompaniments by GEOFFRY RUSSELL-SMITH

INTERNATIONAL MUSIC PUBLICATIONS would like to thank the
following publishers for permission to use arrangements
of their copyright material in TEAM BRASS.
CHAPPELL MUSIC LTD. London W1Y 3FA
for LITTLE DONKEY
© 1959 Chappell Music Ltd.
WARNER BROS MUSIC LTD. London W1P 3DD
for BLOWIN' IN THE WIND
© 1962 (unpub.) © 1963 M Witmark & Sons, USA
and for STAR WARS (Main Title)
© 1977 Fox Fanfare Music Inc. USA
WILLIAMSON MUSIC LTD. London W1Y 3FA
for MY FAVORITE THINGS and EDELWEISS
© 1959 Richard Rodgers & Oscar Hammerstein II
Williamson Music Inc. USA

Sincere thanks are extended
to the following people whose criticism, advice
and help in various ways has been invaluable.
KEITH ALLEN, Senior Instrumental Teacher
for the City of Birmingham.
COLIN MOORE, County Instrumental Organiser
for East Sussex.
BRIAN WICKS, Senior Lecturer at Newman and Westhill
Colleges of Higher Education.
KEITH WATTS, Head of Brass for Sandwell Education Authority.
PETER SMALLEY, Cornet / trumpet player
and Instrumental Teacher, County of Staffordshire.
MOLLY WICKS and PHILIP LEAH, whose enthusiasm
and support have been a great encouragement.

First Published 1988
© Copyright International Music Publications Limited

International Music Publications Limited
Southend Road, Woodford Green,
Essex IG8 8HN

Book Design: Eleanor Gamper
Cover Design: Ian Barrett / Peter White
Cover Photography: Ron Goldby
Production: Peter White / Philip Evry
Reprographics: Positive Colour Ltd.
Instruments photographed by courtesy
of Vincent Bach International Ltd.

TEAM BRASS: Trombone / Euphonium (Bass clef)
ISBN 0 86359 537 5 / Order Ref: 16697 / 215-2-431

Lesson diary & practice chart

Date (week commencing)	Enter number of minutes practised.							Teacher indicates which pages to study.
	Mon	Tue	Wed	Thur	Fri	Sat	Sun	

Getting started

Teachers, who like pupils to experiment with the instrument before learning to use the text, can write helpful notes below, according to the needs of the student.*

Otherwise proceed as follows:
    Starting Note F on page 2, or
    Starting Note B flat on page 4, or
    Group Chords on page 19, or
    Five-Note Patterns on page 11.

*

Lip, jaw and throat positions:

Buzzing with the lips:

Buzzing on the mouthpiece:

Long notes:

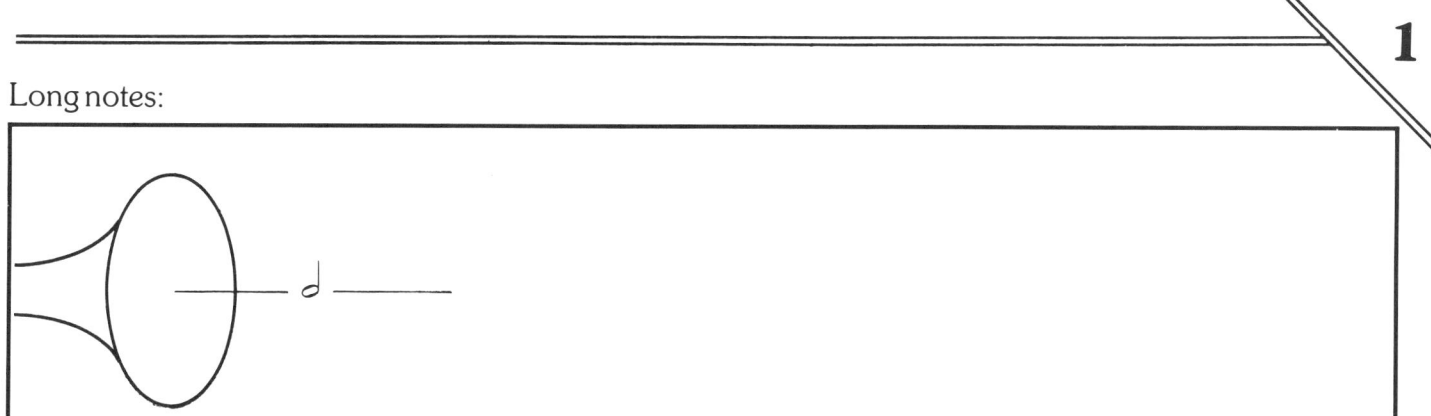

Tongued notes:

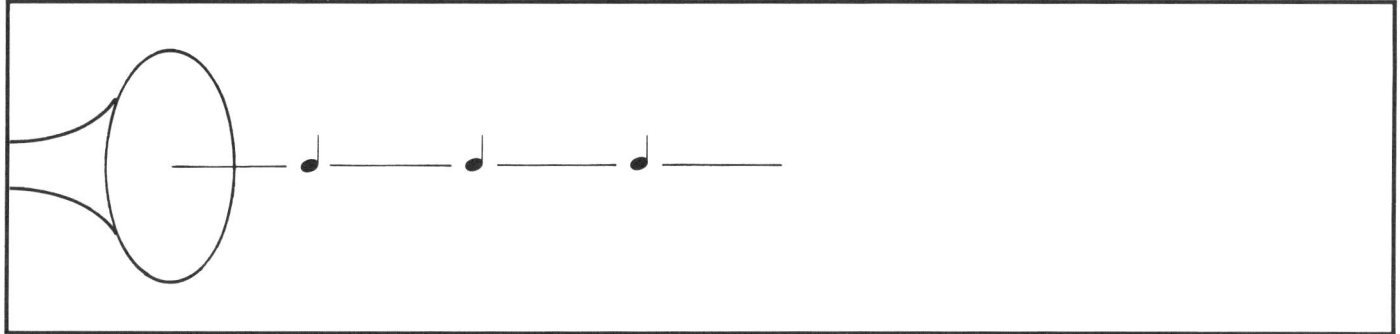

Slurring:

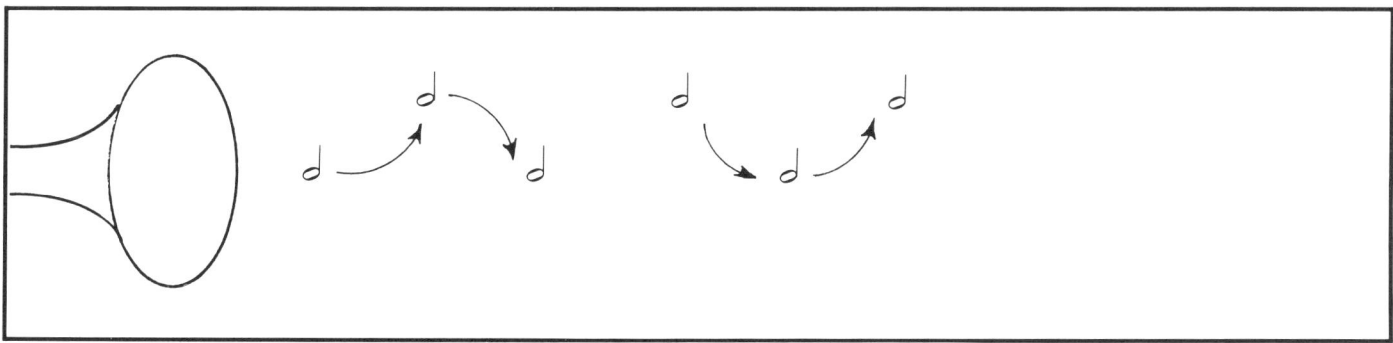

Making up rhythms and melodies, and soundscapes:

All these notes are *possible* on your instrument without using the slide or valves, by merely varying the lip-pressure. At first you will probably only be able to produce the lowest notes.

Start with F . . .

1st position
(open-no valves)

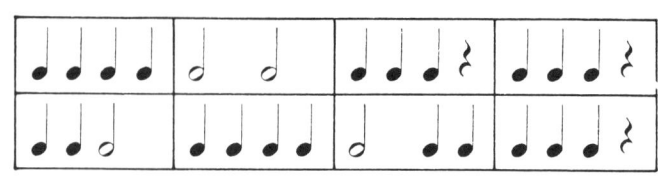

Clap, say,*
and play
the rhythm

Some of the material on pages 2 to 10 integrates with material on other pages in this and other TEAM BRASS books as an aid to group teaching. Follow indications written above appropriate lines.

The TIME-SIGNATURE $\frac{4}{4}$ means each bar must add up to FOUR beats

A MINIM (or HALF-NOTE) lasts for TWO beats

A COMMA means take a breath

A CROTCHET (or QUARTER-NOTE) lasts for ONE beat

A CROTCHET REST lasts for ONE beat

■ Fits with *F Book* page 4, line 2.

■ Fits with *F Book* page 4, line 3.

bar 1   bar 2   bar 3   bar 4

■ Fits with *F Book* page 4, line 4.

■ Fits with page 10, line 1; with *F Book*, page 4, line 5.

RHYTHM

PULSE — clap or beat time

*French time-names may be used.

. . . then on to E flat

Proceed down to D, page 6; or up to G, page 17.

or start with B flat . . .

1st position
(open-no valves)

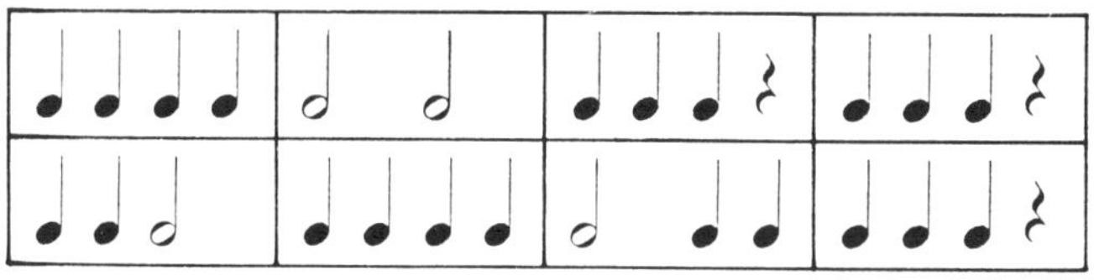

Clap, say,*
and play the
rhythm

The flat sign ♭ is
placed before the note
which is being flattened.
(The other B in the
bar is also flattened)

A MINIM lasts
for TWO beats

A CROTCHET
lasts for ONE beat

The TIME-
SIGNATURE 4/4

means each
bar must
add up to
FOUR beats

A
CROTCHET
REST
lasts for
ONE
beat

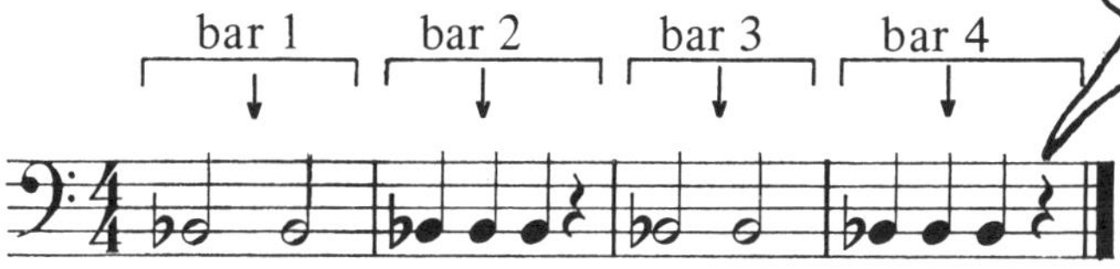

bar 1   bar 2   bar 3   bar 4

A COMMA
means
take a breath

■ Fits with *F Book* page 3, line 2.

RHYTHM

PULSE — clap or
beat time

*French time-names may be used.

...then on to C

6th position
(1st & 3rd valves)

Play the grid across, up, or down

BAR LINES divide a line of notes into sets. In 4/4 time each bar adds up to four crotchet beats

(2 + 1 + 1 = 4)   (1+1+1+1=4)

The DOUBLE BAR marks the end of a piece of music

■ Fits with *F Book* page 3, line 3.   **B♭'s and C's**

■ Fits with *F Book* page 3, line 4.

■ Fits with page 3, line 5.   **Elegy**

Slowly and sadly

■ Proceed up to D, on page 7; or down to A, on page 10.

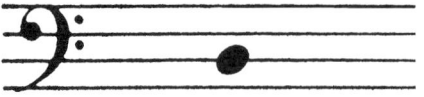

The note D

4th position
(1st & 2nd valves)

■ This page fits harmonically & rhythmically with the one opposite

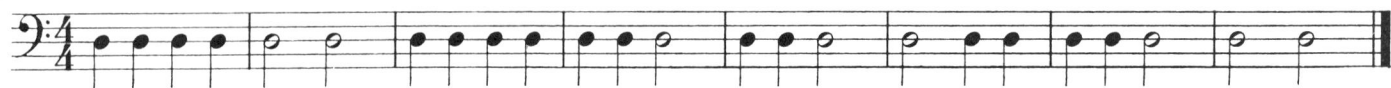

F, E♭ and D together

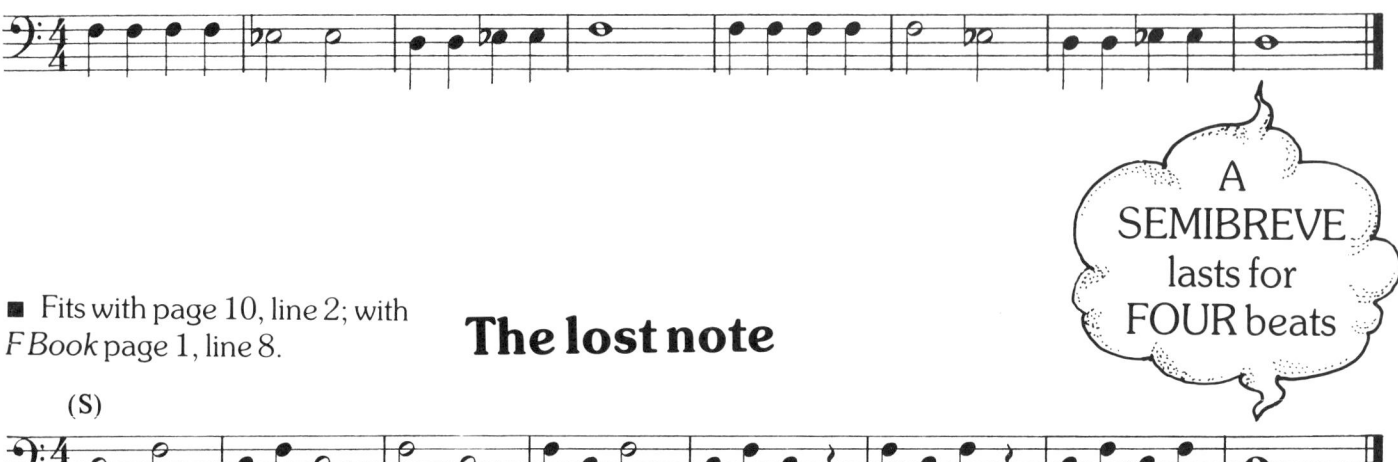

■ Fits with page 10, line 2; with *F Book* page 1, line 8.

The lost note

A SEMIBREVE lasts for FOUR beats

(S)

All mixed up!

(S)

■ This can be played in conjunction with *Acapulco Bay* opposite.

Acapulco Bay

Tempo di Beguine

■ Proceed down to C on page 8; or up to G on page 17.

The 'S' symbol means the music can be slurred throughout (by euphonium players), if the teacher wishes.

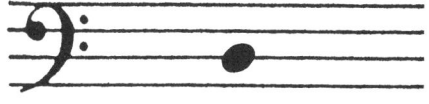

4th position
(1st & 2nd valves) ■ This page fits harmonically & rhythmically with the one opposite.

The note D

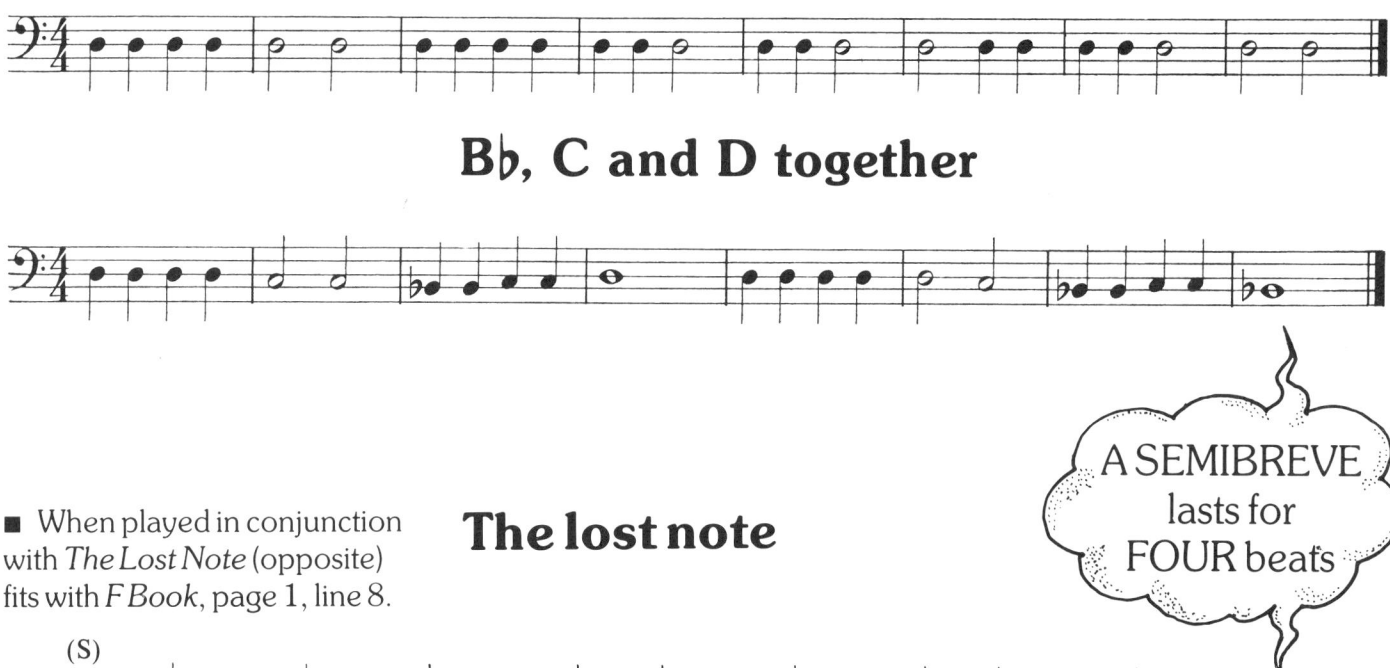

Bb, C and D together

■ When played in conjunction with *The Lost Note* (opposite) fits with *F Book*, page 1, line 8.

The lost note

A SEMIBREVE lasts for FOUR beats

(S)

Tricky tune!

(S)

■ This can be played in conjunction with *Acapulco Bay* opposite.

Acapulco Bay

Tempo di Beguine

■ Proceed up to Eb on page 9; or down to A on page 10.

The 'S' symbol means the music can be slurred throughout (by euphonium players), if the teacher wishes.

F, E♭, D and C together

F	E♭	D	C	D	F	C	E♭	D

Make up your own tunes using these notes

C   ■   If required, see preparatory 'C' exercises on page 5.

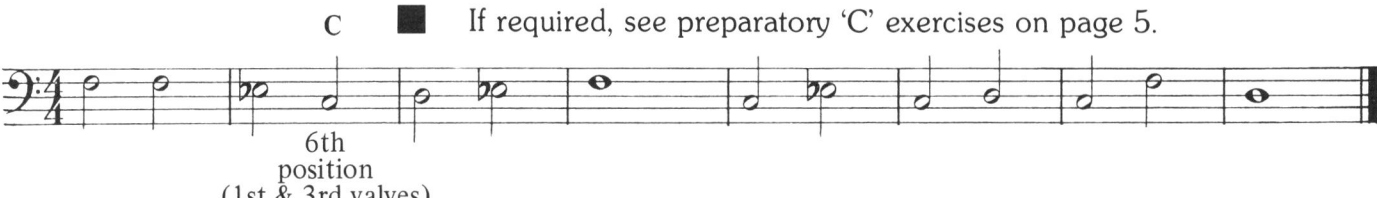

6th
position
(1st & 3rd valves)

■ Fits with page 10, line 4.

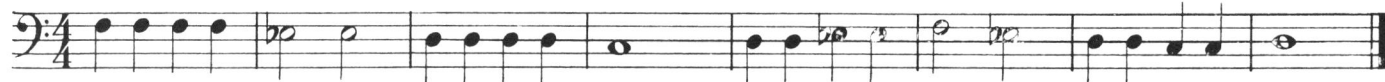

Marching

■ Fits with page 10, line 5.

Gliding

(S)

Vigorous March

Watch your step!

(S)

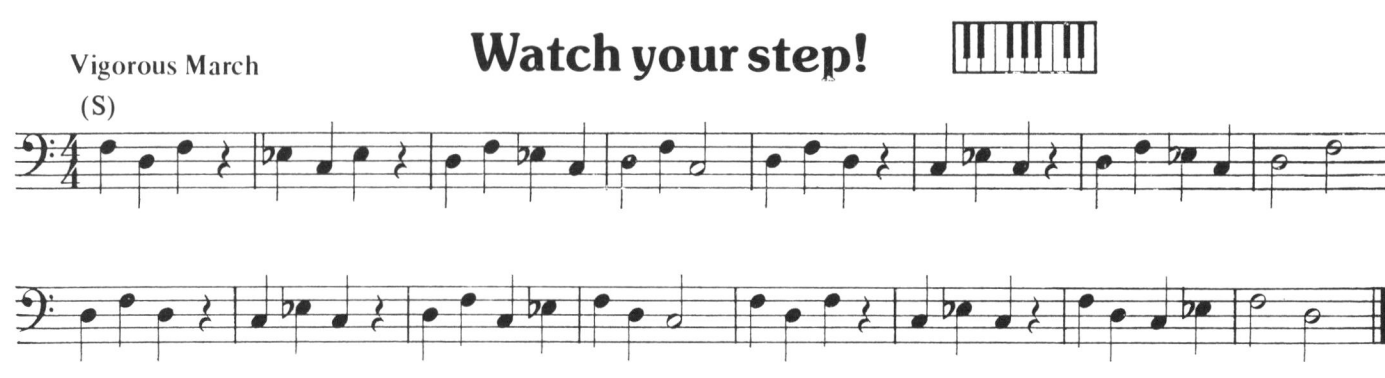

■   *Watch your step!* can be played in conjunction with *Sort 'em out!* (opposite), or with piano accompaniment.

B♭, C, D and E♭ together

D	B♭	C	D	E♭	C	B♭

Make up your own tunes using these notes

E♭

■ If required, see preparatory 'E♭' exercises on page 3.

3rd
position
(1st valve)

Flowing

(S)

Two bar phrase (1)　Two bar phrase (2)　Two bar phrase (3)　Two bar phrase (4)

Walking

Composed by eleven-year old JENNY WONG

Sort 'em out!

March
(S)

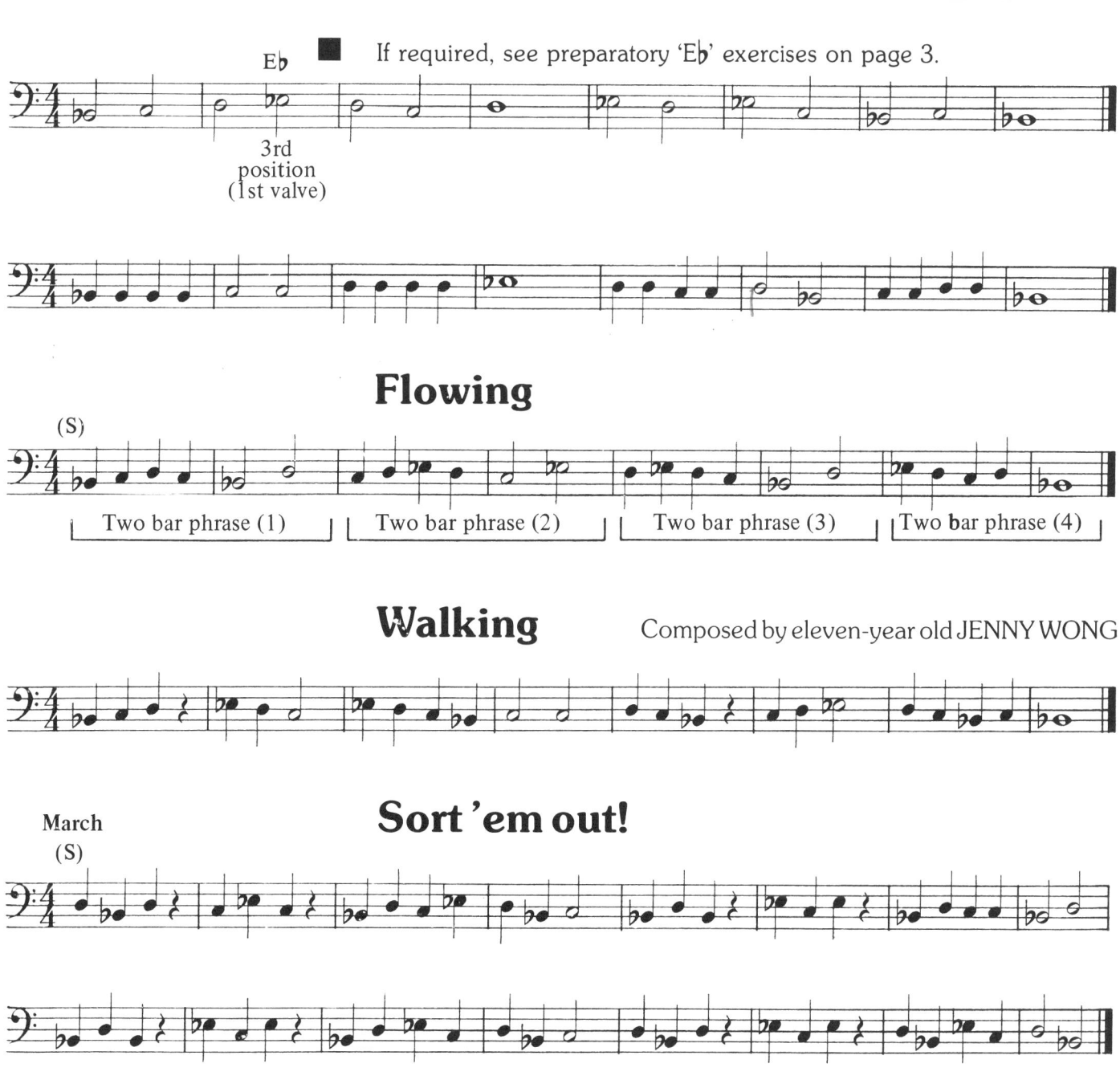

■ *Sort 'em out!* can be played in conjunction with *Watch your step!*
(opposite).

2nd position
(2nd valve)

The note low A

■ All the material on this page integrates with material on previous
pages, as marked.

■ Fits with page 2, line 5; with *F
Book*, page 4, line 5.

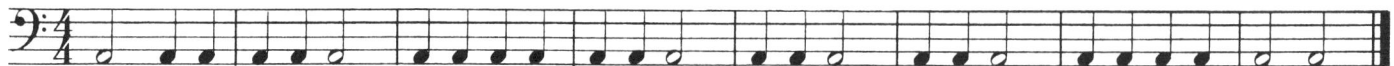

■ Fits with page 6, line 3; with *F
Book*, page 1, line 8.

(S)

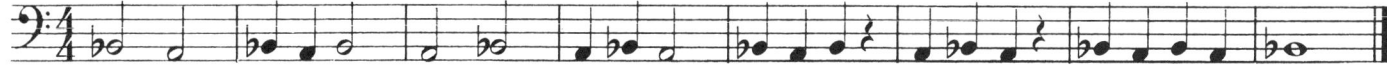

■ Fits with page 6, line 4.

(S)

■ Fits with page 8, line 2.

A with B♭, C and D

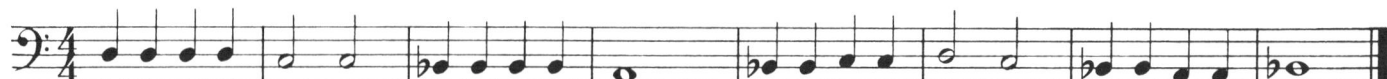

■ Fits with page 8, line 4.

(S)

■ For related ensemble material *see* pages 14, 16, 19, 20, 21.

Five-note patterns

Intervals

Step round

play by ear

Welsh tune

Traditional

New Rhythm

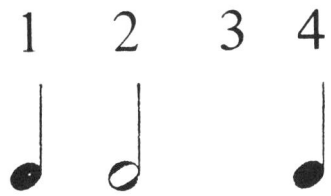

Two rounds

'C' means Common Time i.e. $\frac{4}{4}$ time

Old Liza Jane

Related group 'warm up' on page 19; related ensemble on pages 14 & 15; syncopated ensemble on page 21.

$\frac{3}{4}$ time

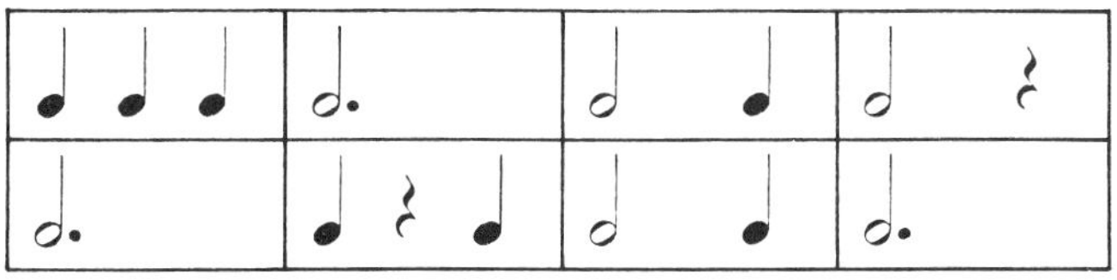

> Every bar adds up to three crotchets

Slow waltz

Composed by
eleven-year old JOANNE AHMED

Four bar question phrase, A   Four bar answer phrase, B

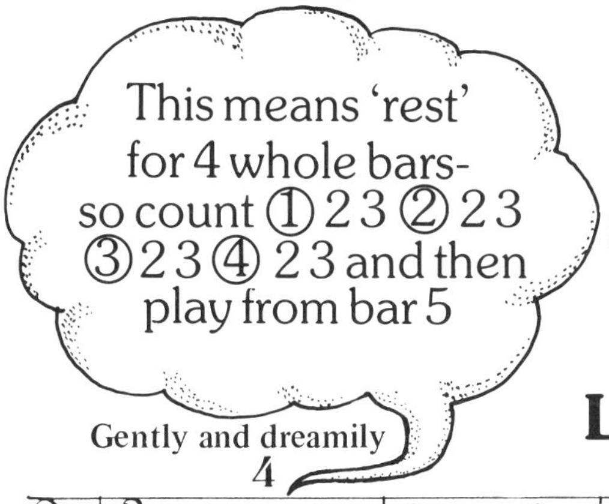

> This means 'rest' for 4 whole bars- so count ① 2 3 ② 2 3 ③ 2 3 ④ 2 3 and then play from bar 5

> A dotted minim lasts for THREE beats

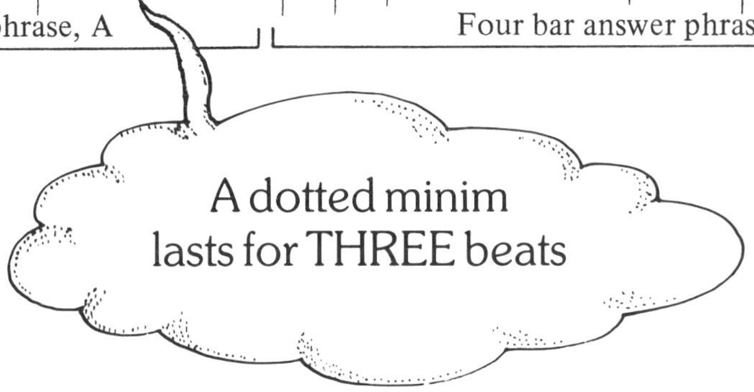

Les ballons

Gently and dreamily

getting slower

(muted, if possible)

Round lullaby

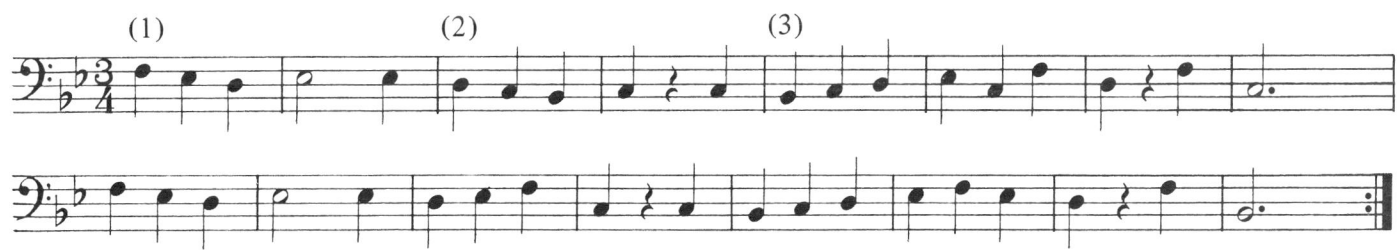

(1)   (2)   (3)

■ Proceed up to G, page 17; or to quavers, page 22; or E♮, page 24; or low G, page 36.

German tune

(Bass part with *Trumpet* duet)*

Traditional

Lullaby

(Bass part with *Trumpet* duet)*

German tune

DUET

Traditional

Third and fourth parts to trombone duets appear in the *F horn book* and the supplement to the brass band book.

*This part can also be played with the *Trombone* duets.

Tied notes

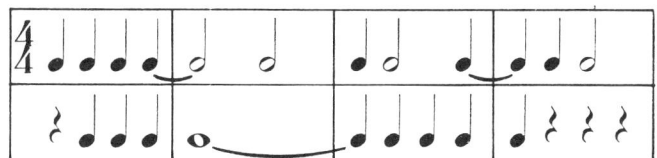

A minim tied to a crotchet lasts for 3 beats.

A crotchet tied to a crotchet lasts for 2 beats.

A semibreve tied to a crotchet lasts for 5 beats and so on.

Don't be late!

(S)

Tied on the slide

This means 'rest' for 5 bars — so count ① 2 3 4 ② 2 3 4 etc. . . then play from bar 6

Canzonetta

(Bass part with *Trumpet* duet)

Fast

5

(Polyphonic texture) *(soft)*

A (Homophonic texture)

(loud)

More tied notes on pages 18, 20 and 21. Preparatory rounds on pages 11 & 12.

Slide	Valves
1	Open
2	2nd
3	1st
4	1st & 2nd
5	2nd & 3rd

Slurs (1)
and legato tonguing

Play all slurs with different slide positions or valve combinations

Slide slur/legato tonguing

German tune

(Third part with *F Horn* duet)

Traditional

Lullaby

(Third part with *F Horn* duet)

COUNT
① 2 3 ② 2 3

① 2 3 ② 2 3

Proceed up to G, or to 'quavers' on page 22; or to E♮ on page 24; or to low G on page 36. *German Tune* for Trombone duet on page 14.

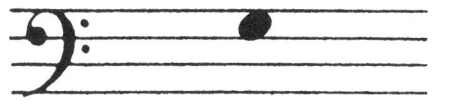

4th position
(1st & 2nd valves)

The note G

play these
notes using
varied
rhythm patterns

B♭	E♭	G
E♭	G	G
A	D	D
D	A	D

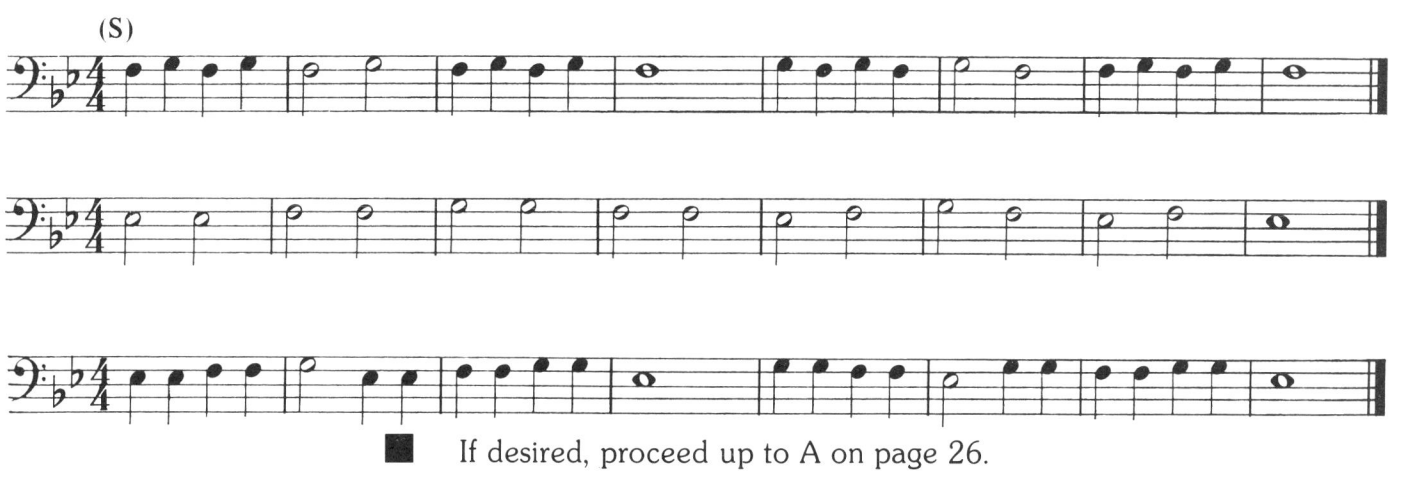

(S)

■ If desired, proceed up to A on page 26.

Pattern
(Based on the QUADRATONE)

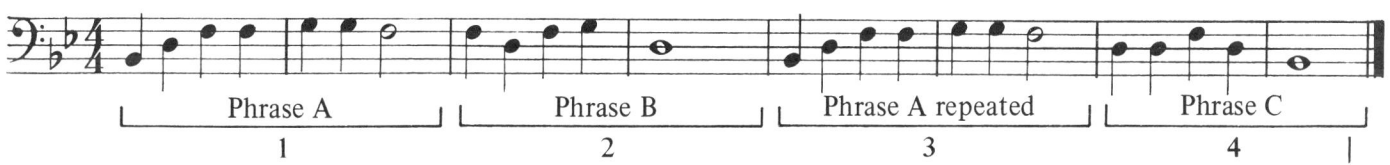

Phrase A	Phrase B	Phrase A repeated	Phrase C
1	2	3	4

Slow round

(1) (2)

play by ear

 Continue

 Continue

■ *see Accompaniments Book concerning the QUADRATONE.*

New rhythms

Make up your own tunes using these rhythms

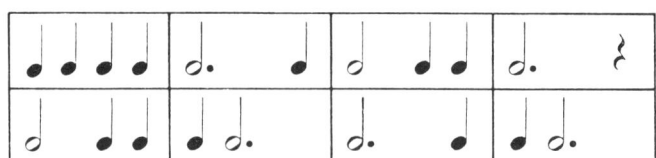

(1)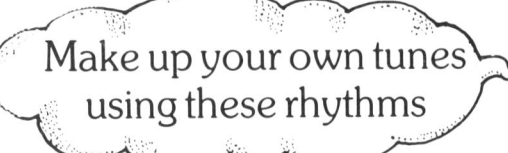

(2)

(3)

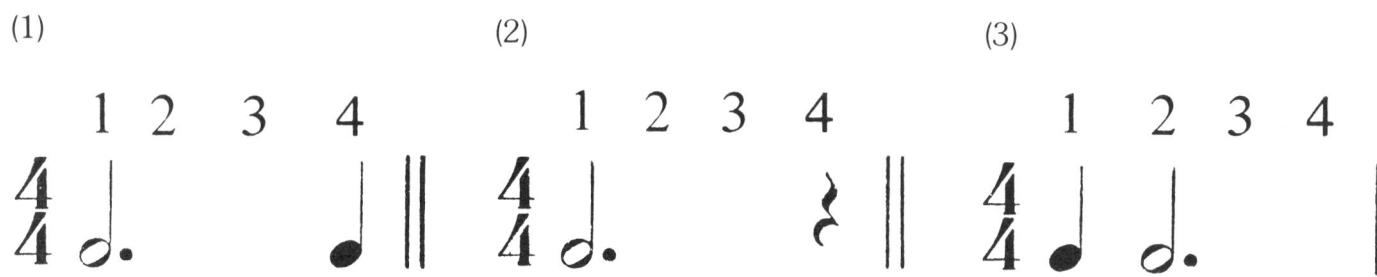

Phrase A (upwards) — 1 | Phrase B (upwards) — 2 | Phrase A (downwards) — 3 | Phrase B (downwards) — 4

3 + 1 = 4

Stepping out

Strident and fast

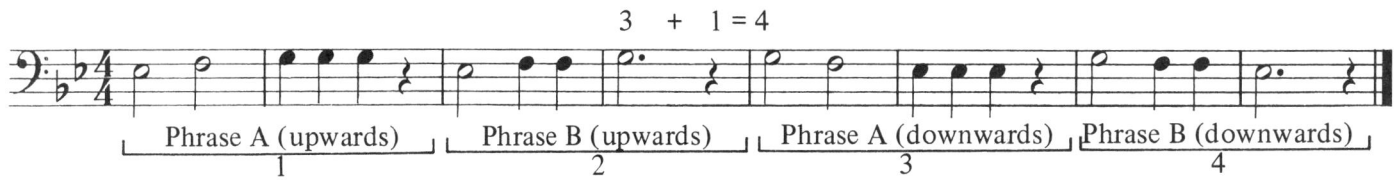

When the saints go marching in

Bouncy

Traditional

■ Proceed to Low G, page 36; or up to A on page 26; or to A♭ on page 32; or to Quavers on page 22; or to E♮ on page 24. Related ensemble on pages 20 & 21.

Brass group warm-up 1

is the sign for PAUSE, meaning the note should be held beyond its normal value

Harmony long notes

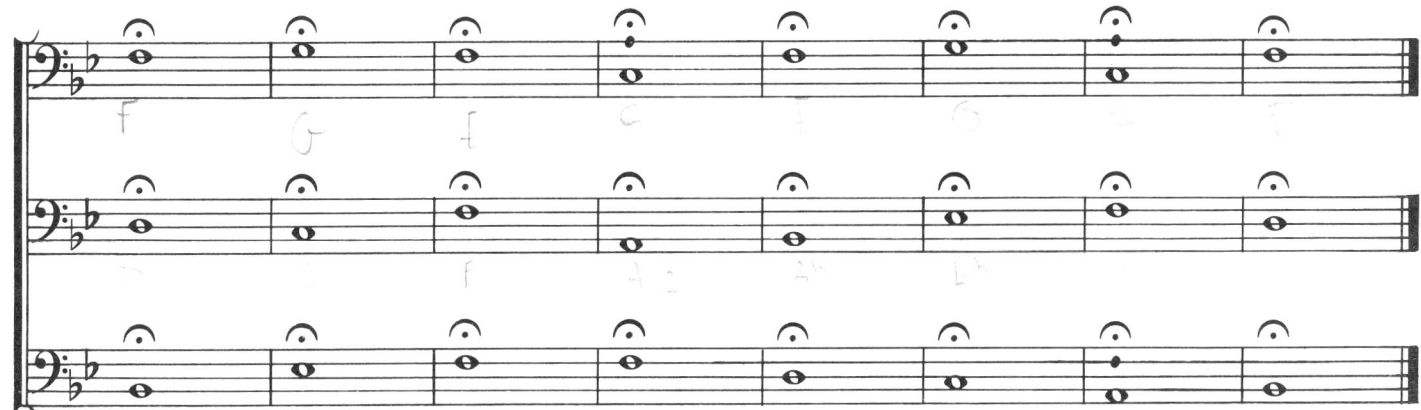

Practise tonguing on each note, devising your own rhythm patterns

When only two players are available, use 2nd and 3rd parts

Unison long notes

(optional)

Slurred slow notes

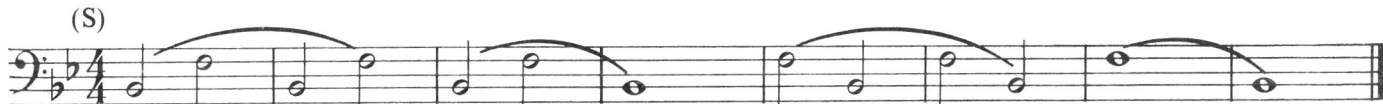

Slurred fast notes

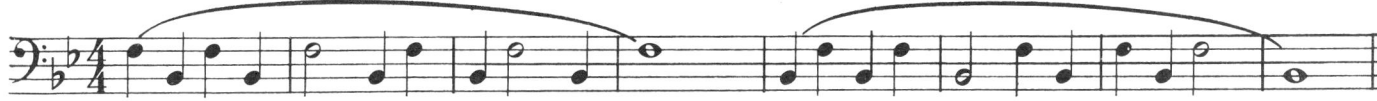

Regal fanfare

(Bass part with *Trumpet* ensemble)

Maestoso

> ₵ means TWO MINIM BEATS in each bar, ie $\frac{2}{2}$ time.
> (Sometimes called ALLA BREVE time)

When I first came to this land

(Bass part with *Trumpet* duet)

Traditional

Fast and furious

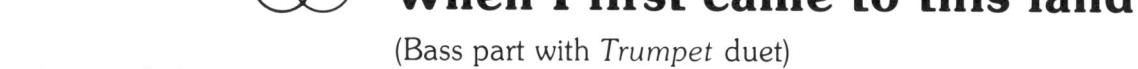

When I first came to this land

DUET

Traditional

Fast and furious

On the repeat, omit these bars and go straight to the bar marked 2

Blowin' in the wind

(Bass part with *Trumpet* duet)

Words and music by BOB DYLAN

Blowin' in the wind

DUET

Words and music by BOB DYLAN

Accompaniment for synthesizer on 'samba' rhythm setting

Play three times, then on to 'chorus'

4/4	Bb	Eb	F	Bb	Bb	Eb	F	F7

Chorus

Eb	F	Bb	Gmin	Eb	F	Bb	Bb

Quavers in $\frac{4}{4}$ time

Here we go!

Words and music by
eleven-year old JOANNE O'NEILL

■ Syncopated quavers on page 44; quavers in $\frac{6}{8}$ on page 41; dotted-crotchet-quaver on page 42; related ensemble on pages 20, 37 & 49.

Quavers in ¾ & ²⁄₄ time

■ ²⁄₄ Rhythm Grid on page 34.

(2 + 1=3)

Roundabout

(1) (2) (3) (4)

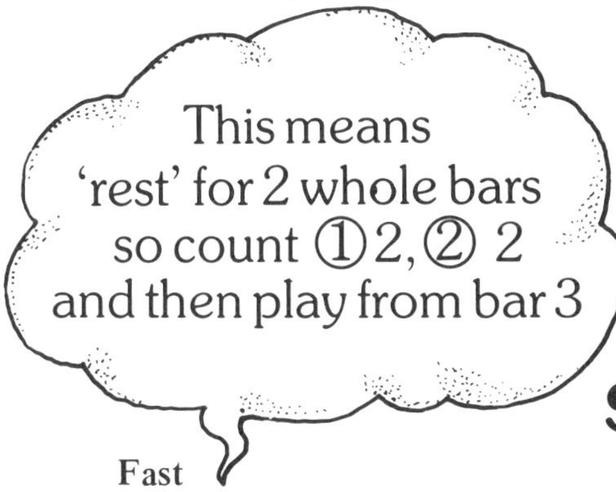

> This means 'rest' for 2 whole bars so count ①2, ②2 and then play from bar 3

> Make up your own tune about something that moves quickly using quavers

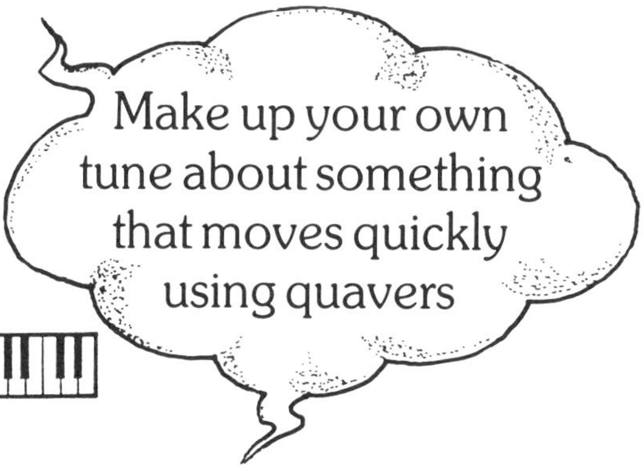

Sleigh ride

Fast

2

loud

fairly loud

very loud

The note E natural

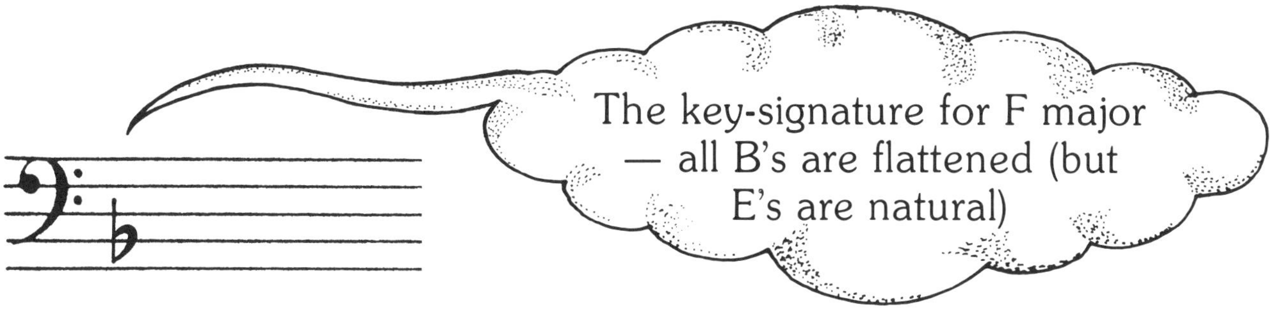

The key-signature for F major
— all B's are flattened (but
E's are natural)

Slavic slurs

Smoothly

■ To be played with *legato tonguing or slide slurring* throughout, as
directed.

The natural sign

The NATURAL cancels
the effect of a flat (or a
sharp)

Austrian Holiday
Eb/E♮ Study

Lilting

(Accent)

Fine   *slower*

D.C. al Fine
a tempo

■ Related ensemble on page 37.

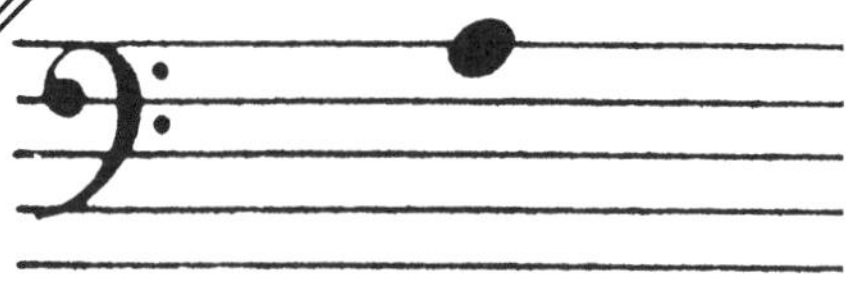

The note A

2nd position
(2nd valve)

Sing hosanna

(S) Merrily

Traditional

Victorian ballad

(S) In relaxed style

Fine

D.C. al Fine

This stands for
DA CAPO AL FINE, which
means go back to the
beginning and end at the
bar marked FINE

A flat (page 32) can be introduced before A, if desired.

Workin' on the railroad

Like a jolly cowboy saloon song

Traditional

(2 + 2 = 4)

$\frac{5}{4}$ time

Waiting!

play by ear

Continue

Continue

Relevant ensemble: A with quavers, page 37.

Upper B♭

1st position
(open)

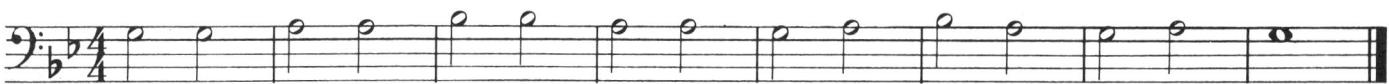

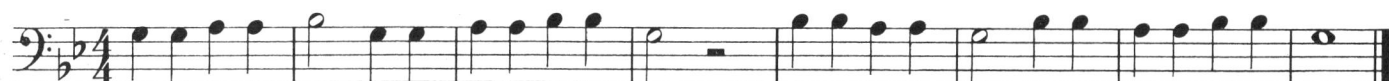

Scale and arpeggio of B♭

B♭ chromatic scale

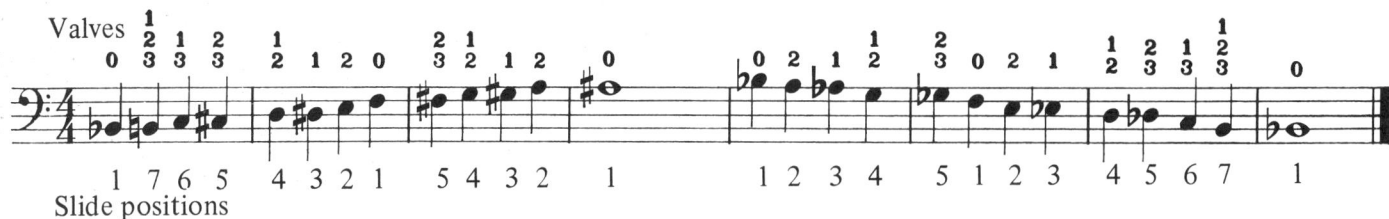

Intervals

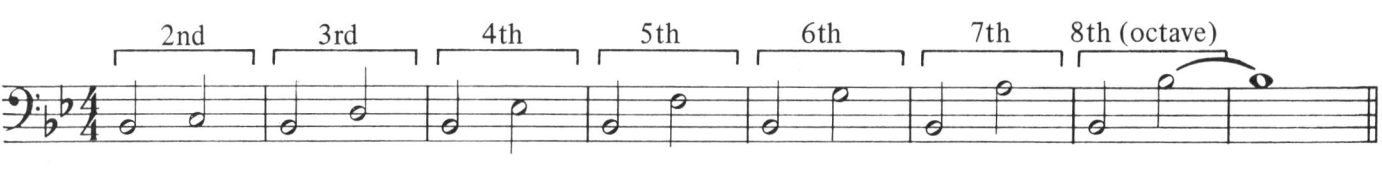

■ Extended chromatic scale on page 55.

UNIQUE FEATURES OF

1. TEAM BRASS REPERTOIRE is suitable for individual, group and class use.

2. TEAM BRASS REPERTOIRE offers students an extremely wide diversity of musical styles from the Baroque period to Jazz, including Classical, Film, Folk, T.V., Hymnal and Opera.

3. The material in TEAM BRASS REPERTOIRE is carefully graded in range and difficulty from the beginner stage to approximately grade 4 standard and can therefore be used in conjunction with any brass tutor - particularly the TEAM BRASS series.

4. Many of the pieces presented in TEAM BRASS REPERTOIRE are brass orientated works in their original form, such as *Match of the Day* and *Coronation Street*.

5. Each book contains many trios which can be extended into quartets by using other TEAM BRASS REPERTOIRE books.

6. The trios in TEAM BRASS REPERTOIRE can all be played as duets simply by omitting the third (inessential) part.

7. The ensemble material in TEAM BRASS REPERTOIRE is suitable for both orchestral brass and brass band players.

Scarborough Fair

Traditional

The pink panther

By HENRY M

A WIDE VARIETY OF MUSICAL STYLES TO SUIT ALL TASTES.

THE THIRD PART OMITTED TO A DUET.

SAMPLE PAGES (REDUCED) FROM

When the saints go marching in

Fast and jazzy

Traditional

© 1989 International Music Publications, Woodford Green, Essex. IG8 8HN

For improvisation, the chord sequence (above) may be used. The following more varied sequence will also fit this tune:—

Accompaniment for electronic keyboard on JAZZ ROCK.

Bb	Bb	Bb	Bb	Bb	Bb	F	F
Bb	Bb7	Eb	Ebm	Bb	C7	F7	Bb	Bb

N.B. Fourth parts to trumpet trios can be found in the Trombone, F Horn and Brass Band books.

A CHORD SEQUENCE IS PROVIDED FOR AN OPTIONAL ELECTRONIC KEYBOARD ACCOMPANIMENT AND/OR IMPROVISATION.

8. Each TEAM BRASS REPERTOIRE book contains a supplement of clear scores for all the ensemble material.

9. In addition to ensemble material, TEAM BRASS REPERTOIRE contains many solo pieces presented in a variety of styles.

10. Accompaniment chord symbols for B flat, E flat and F instruments are provided in appropriate pieces.

11. The content of TEAM BRASS REPERTOIRE is suitable for solo or group performance in assembly, concert, music centre and festival events.

12. Each TEAM BRASS REPERTOIRE book contains concise notes on jazz improvisation for B flat, E flat and F instruments. Extended improvisation is encouraged in jazz pieces such as *Don't Sit Under the Apple Tree* and *Little Brown Jug.*

13. The improvisational element presented in TEAM BRASS REPERTOIRE makes it eminently suitable for those pupils who are following GCSE music courses.

14. TEAM BRASS REPERTOIRE contains 32 action packed titles making it excellent value for money.

TEAM BRASS REPERTOIRE

TEAM BRASS REPERTOIRE has been specially designed to complement the TEAM BRASS TUTOR SERIES*, but can be used in conjunction with any other brass tutor. It will be appealing to young brass players and teachers everywhere. Each of the four books contain carefully graded music which presents a wide diversity of styles to cater for the individual pupil's interest.

TEAM BRASS REPERTOIRE allows the teacher to work with an individual or a group of players. The instrumental books are interrelated and repertoire pieces are provided for solo instrument with chord symbol accompaniment, two or three like instruments, and mixed brass ensemble. TEAM BRASS REPERTOIRE also introduces and encourages jazz improvisation through several jazz pieces.

*A colour descriptive leaflet on the TEAM BRASS TUTOR SERIES is available from the Education Division at the address below.

TEAM BRASS REPERTOIRE covers:

Ref		Price	Qty
17161	**TRUMPET/CORNET**	**£3.95**	
17162	**FRENCH HORN**	**£3.95**	
17163	**TROMBONE/EUPHONIUM** (Bass Clef)	**£3.95**	
17164	**BRASS BAND INSTRUMENTS**	**£3.95**	

published by

 **International Music Publications**

Woodford Trading Estate, Southend Road, Woodford Green, Essex IG8 8HN, England.
Telephone: 081-551 6131   International: +44 81 551 6131   Fax: 081-551 3919

Look for scale patterns

Round the scale

(S) (1) (2)

forte

mezzo forte

forte

You will find a GLOSSARY of musical terms on page 62

Study in B♭

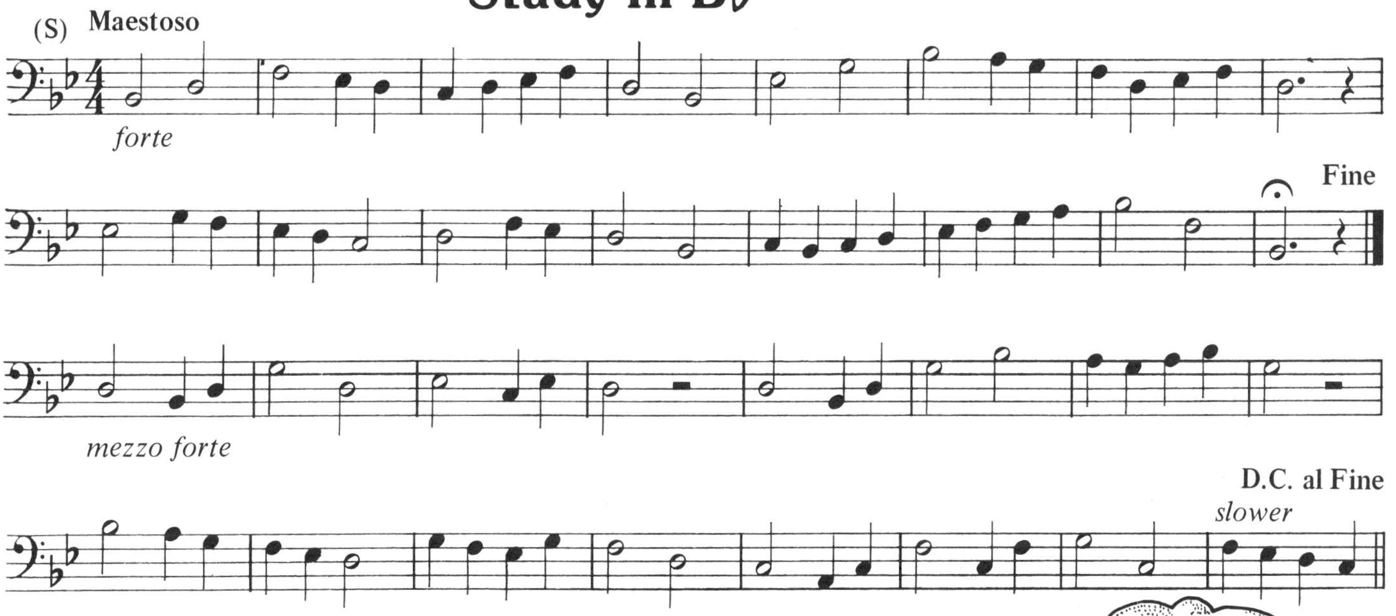

(S) **Maestoso**

forte

Fine

mezzo forte

D.C. al Fine
slower

Play by ear

Try playing by ear, your favourites from the world of classics, pop or TV.

Continue

Continue

Slide	Valves
1	Open
2	2nd
3	1st
4	1st & 2nd
5	2nd & 3rd
6	1st & 3rd
7	1st, 2nd & 3rd

Slurs (2)

And slide slurs/legato tonguing

■ Delete anacrusis as necessary.

Play all slurs with different slide positions or valve combinations

Slide slur/legato tonguing

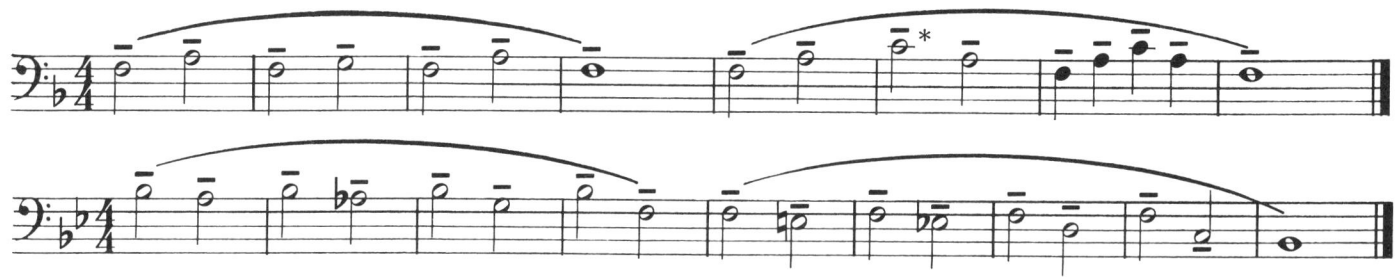

Blowin' in the wind

(Third part with *F Horn* duet)

Words and music
by BOB DYLAN

■ *Blowin' in the wind* for trombone duet on page 21.
Upper C on page 35.

Plainchant

Play 'freely', i.e. not with a strict pulse

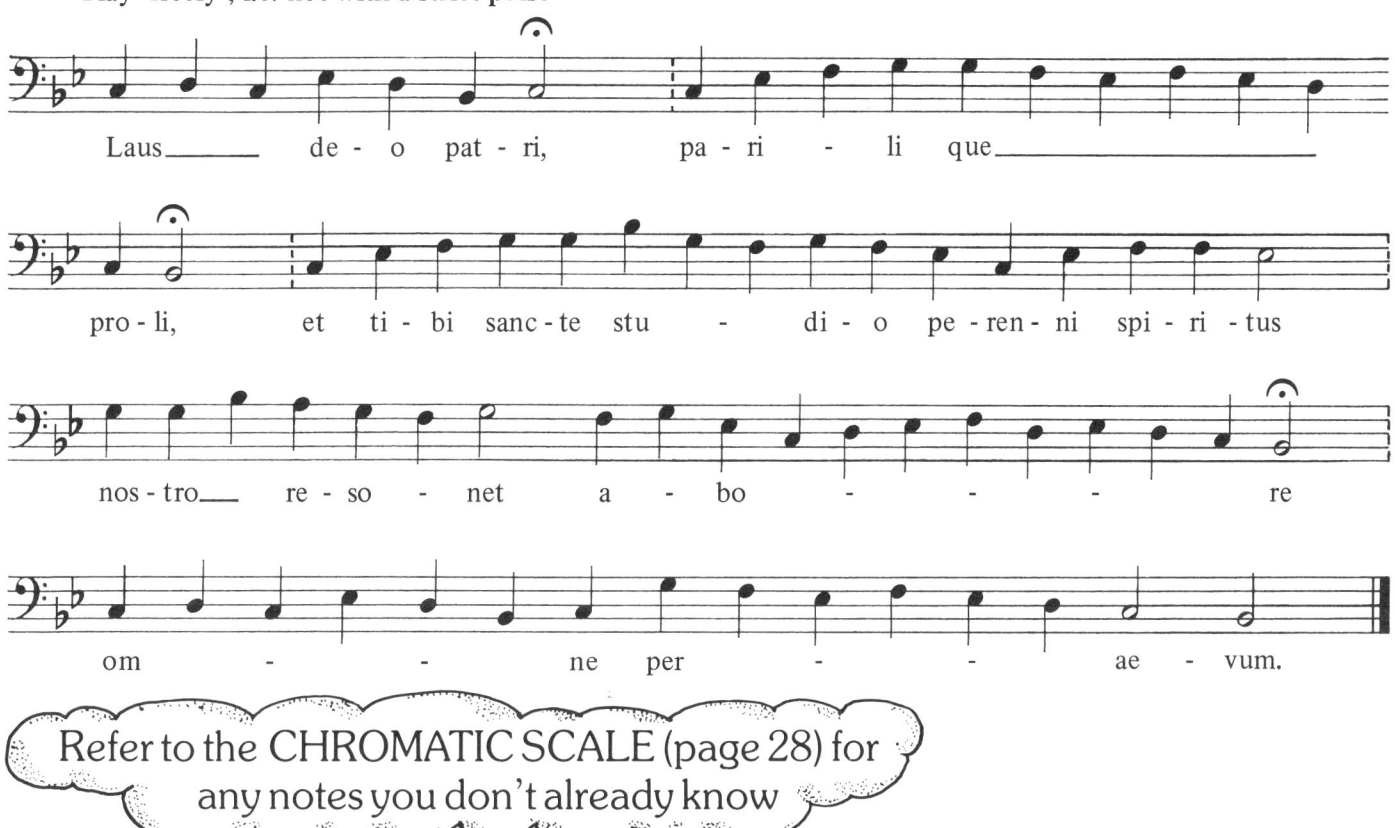

Laus____ de - o pat - ri, pa - ri - li que____

pro - li, et ti - bi sanc - te stu - di - o pe - ren - ni spi - ri - tus

nos - tro____ re - so - net a - bo - re

om - ne per - ae - vum.

Refer to the CHROMATIC SCALE (page 28) for any notes you don't already know

My favourite things

From *The Sound of Music*

Words by OSCAR HAMMERSTEIN II
Music by RICHARD RODGERS

Chromatic scale on page 28. Proceed up to C, page 35; or down to G, page 36; or to A♭, page 32; or to quavers, page 34.

The note A flat

3rd position
(1st valve)

The FLAT lowers the pitch of a note by one semitone

E♭	F	G	A♭	D	G	E♭
B♭	A♭	C	F	E♭	B♭	D

C minor round

We wish you a Merry Christmas   Traditional

Fast and jolly

play by ear

■ Related ensemble, page 54; E♭ scale, page 56; C minor scale, page 58.

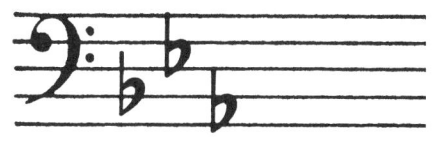

Key-signature of E♭ major C minor

Yankee Doodle

Traditional

Aura Lee

Traditional

E♭ major round

Coventry carol

Traditional

*Upper C on page 35.

Relaxation

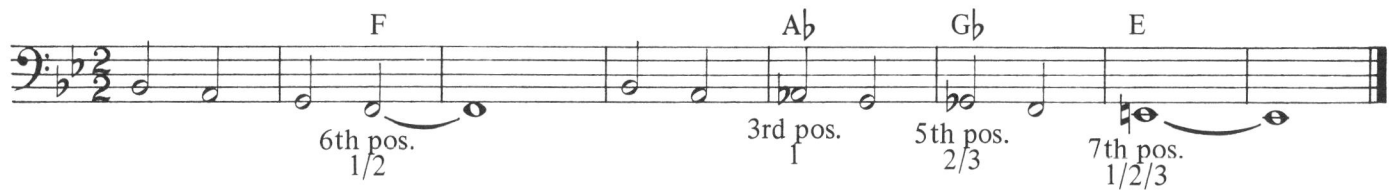

Quavers up to B♭

---

mf   *crescendo*   *f*   *diminuendo*   *mf*

mf   *f*   *mf*

Quaver study

Allegro

mf   *f*

mf   *f*

mf   *f*

mf   *f*

mf   *f*

mf   *f*

■ Syncopated quavers on page 44; semiquavers on page 40; dotted crotchet on page 42; ⁶₈ quavers on page 41; dotted quavers on page 50.

Upper C

The small line above the stave is called a LEGER LINE

3rd position
(1st valve)

Limp round

(1) (2) (3)

Edelweiss

From *The Sound of Music*

words by OSCAR HAMMERSTEIN II
music by RICHARD RODGERS

Semplice

mp

f

rall. . . . .

play by ear

Continue

Continue

■ ⁶⁄₈ up to C, page 54; quavers up to C, pages 39, 45; semiquavers up to C, page 40. Relaxation exercises on page 33. Dotted crotchet/quaver, page 42.

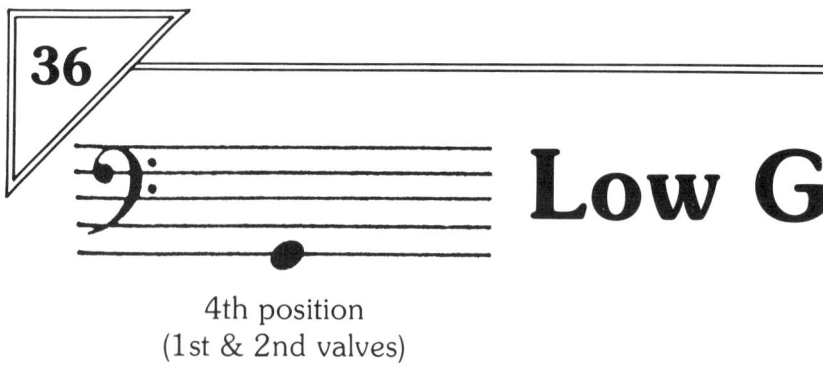

Low G

4th position
(1st & 2nd valves)

(S)

Quadratone pattern

Compose your own
piece using the notes of
the QUADRATONE*

Low round

(1)   (2)

mp

Theme from Polovtsian dances

ALEXANDER BORODIN (1833-87)

Lilting, not fast

mp – (*mf*)

■ Related ensemble on pages 37 and 48.
*A useful group of notes requiring 1st & 4th position (open and 1/2
fingering only).

Au claire de la lune

Traditional

(Bass part with *Trumpet* duet)

Little donkey

words and music by ERIC BOSWELL

(Bass part with *Trumpet* duet)

Au claire de la lune

Traditional

DUET

Little donkey

Words and music by ERIC BOSWELL

DUET

Brass group warm-up 2

Harmony long notes

> When only two players are available, use 2nd and 3rd parts

> Make up word- or name-rhythms for tonguing practice

Unison long notes

(1) *piano*   (2) *mezzo forte*   (3) *forte*   (4) *piano*

Scale exercise

piano crescendo forte diminuendo piano   *p ——— f ——— p ——— f*

Slurs

(1)

(2)

■ More level (2) slurs on page 30.

Tijuana brass

(Bass part with *Trumpet* duet)

Tijuana brass

DUET

I saw three ships

(Bass part with *Trumpet* duet)

Traditional

■ *I saw three ships* for trombone duet on page 54.

Semiquavers in $\frac{2}{4}$

(Start slowly)

Semiquaver study

Allegro

Fine

D.C. al Fine

Join the dots in order to make 'ties' as and when required

Related ensemble on pages 48 and 55.

Related ensemble on page 54.

The dotted crotchet in $\frac{4}{4}$

Make up your own melodies using dotted rhythms

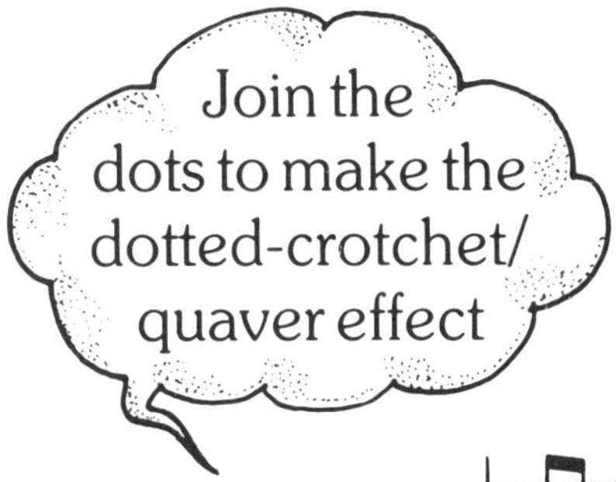

Join the dots to make the dotted-crotchet/quaver effect

Theme

from "*New World*" Symphony

ANTONIN DVOŘÁK
(1841-1904)

Quick march

Composed by nine-year old
REBECKA ELEY

'Ode to joy'

LUDWIG VAN BEETHOVEN
(1770-1827)

Allegro assai

f

mp

f

Play by ear

Continue

Continue

■ Related ensemble on pages 48 and 54.

The dotted crotchet in $\frac{3}{4}$ and $\frac{2}{4}$

> Compose your own piece about an interesting place or far-away country

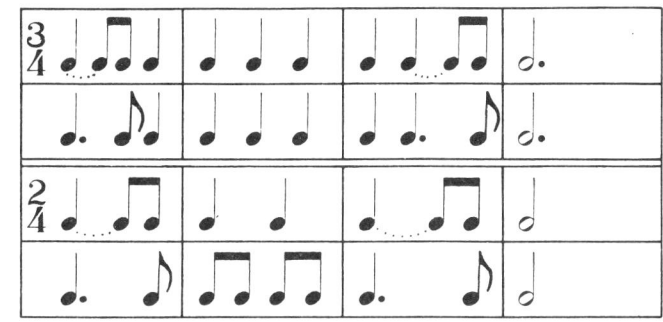

Legato e cantabile 🎹

Scottish ballad

mf

p

Fine

D.S. al Fine

> D.S. al Fine stands for DAL SEGNO (meaning go back to the SIGN, bar 3) and stop at the bar marked FINE

Rickshaws

> Based on the QUADRATONE

f

Fine

D.C. al Fine

p

■ *See Accompaniments Book* concerning the QUADRATONE.

Quaver syncopation

To be played (A) in strict time
and (B) in swinging time

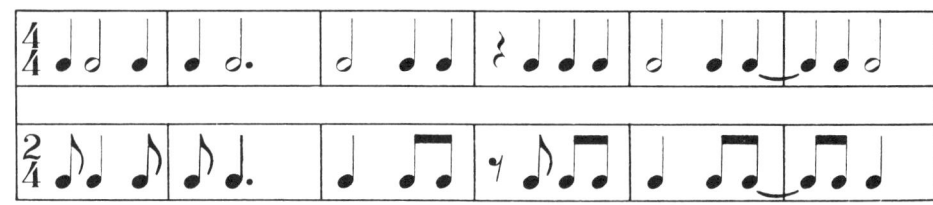

Old Liza Jane

See Glossary for new signs

Caribbean dance

Traditional

Tempo di Rumba

f

Fine

p

D.C. al Fine

Play by ear

Continue

■ Syncopated crotchets on pages 12, 15 and 21; Related ensemble on page 39. *Upper D on page 50.

Simply blue
Twelve bar blues

Slow dance style (♩=80)

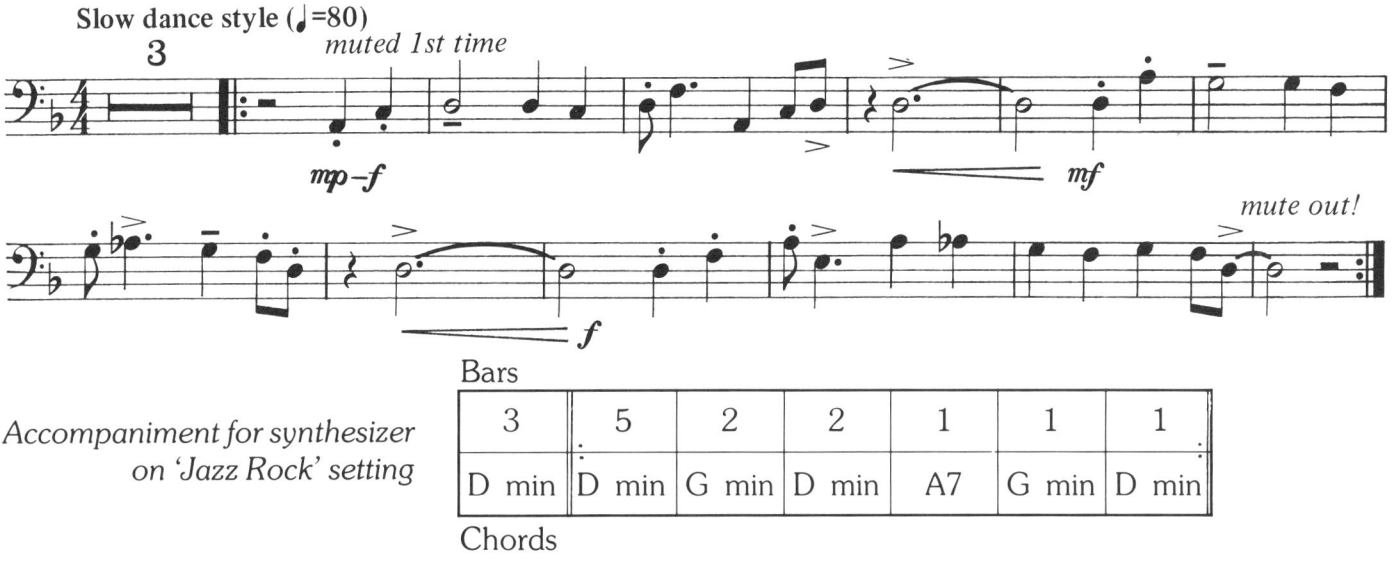

Bars						
3	5	2	2	1	1	1
D min	D min	G min	D min	A7	G min	D min

Accompaniment for synthesizer on 'Jazz Rock' setting

Chords

West Indian carnival

Very fast and rhythmic

Au claire de la lune

(Third part with *F Horn* duet)

Traditional

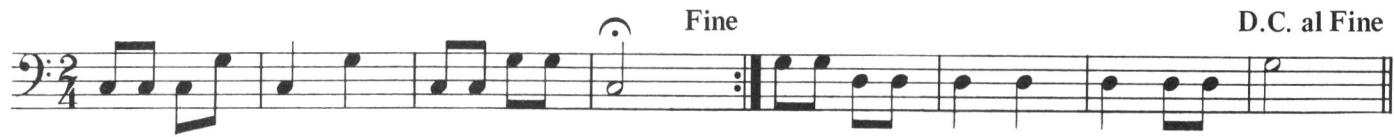

Little donkey

(Third part with *F Horn* duet)

Words and Music
by ERIC BOSWELL

L. A. Nitespot

Twelve bar blues

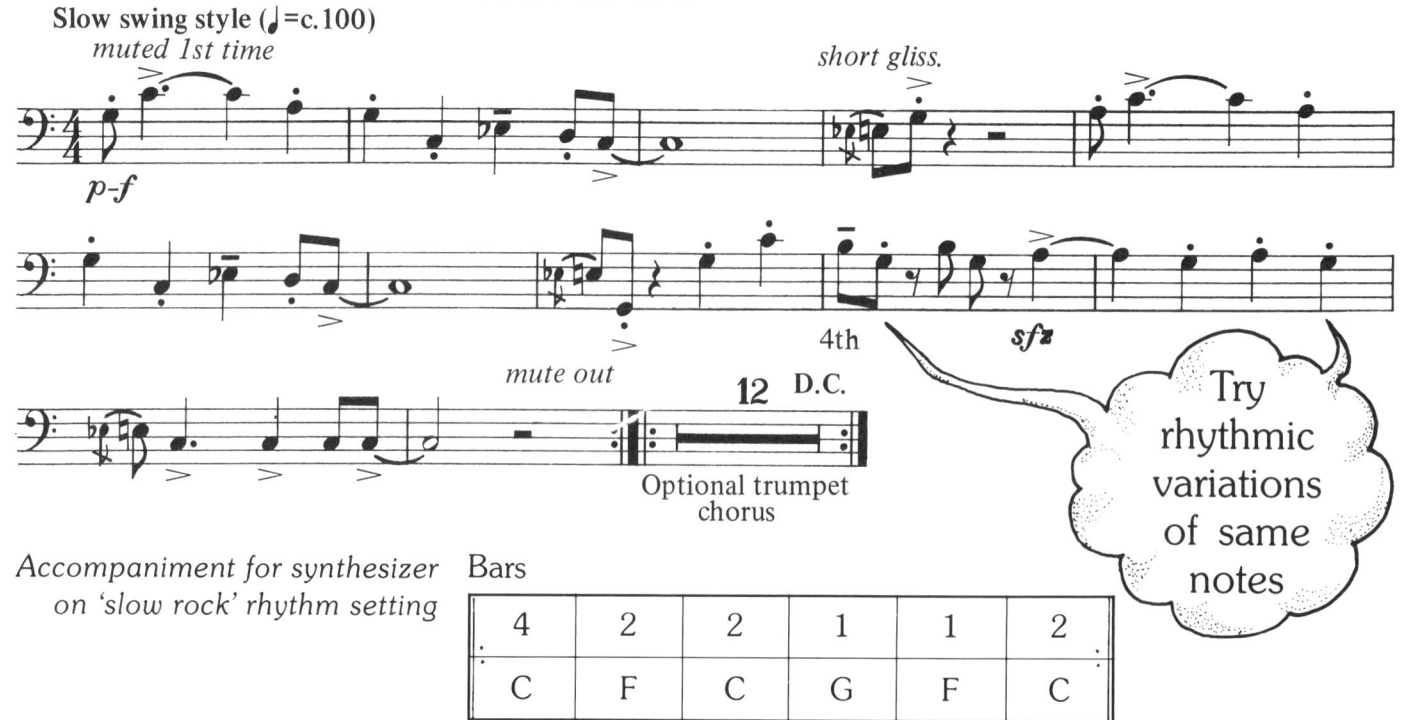

Accompaniment for synthesizer on 'slow rock' rhythm setting

Bars					
4	2	2	1	1	2
C	F	C	G	F	C

■ Scale of C minor on page 58.   Chords

Regal fanfare

(Bass part with *F Horn* ensemble)

When I first came to this land

(Third part with *F Horn* duet)

Regal fanfare

Timpani (or bass drum and tenor drum) and cymbals.

When I first came to this land for trombone duet, page 20.

Michael row the boat

(Bass part with *Trumpet* duet)

Traditional

Canzona

(Part 4)

(*See Trumpet* book)

ADRIANO BANCHIERI (1568-1634)

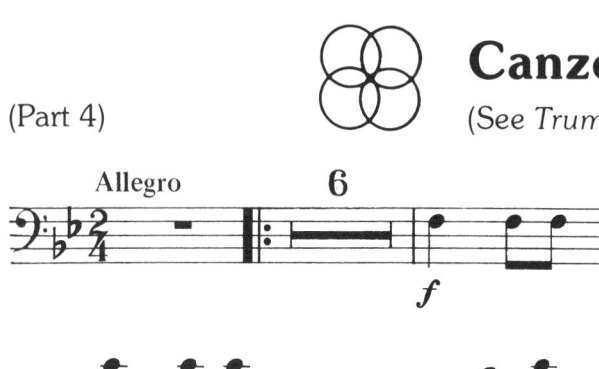

(Part 3)

Michael row the boat

DUET

Traditional

O Little Town of Bethlehem

(Bass part with *Trumpet* duet)

Traditional

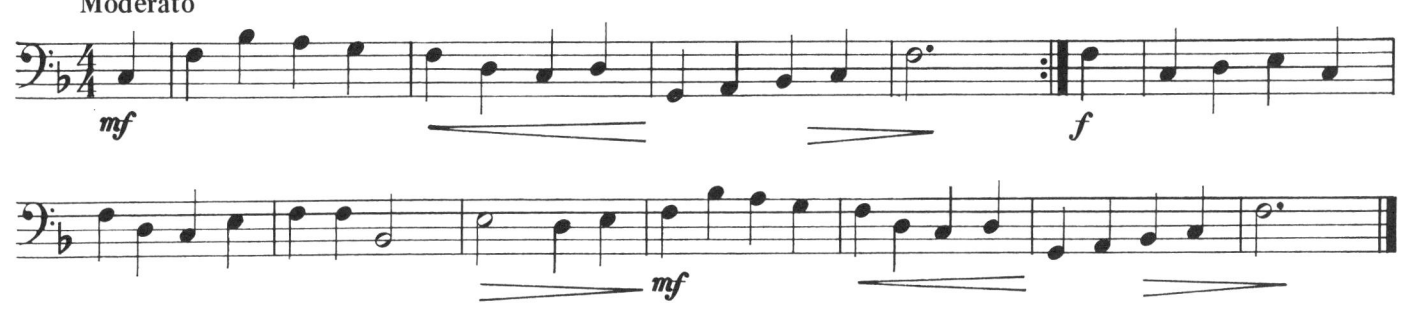

St. Anthony chorale

(Bass part with *Trumpet* duet)

JOSEPH HAYDN (1732-1809)

O Little Town of Bethlehem

DUET

Traditional

■ *St. Anthony chorale* for Trombone duet on page 54.

Upper D

1st position
(open)

I gave my love a cherry

Traditional

Andante cantabile

The dotted quaver

Theme

Canon

Gustav Mahler (1860-1911)

Langsam

■ 'Relaxation' exercises on page 33.

Say 'goodbye'

From the opera *Marriage of Figaro*

WOLFGANG AMADEUS MOZART (1756-1791)

Triplet quaver group - Three quavers played in the time of one crotchet

Old Spanish town

Extra material up to D on pages 44, 48, 49, 58 and 59.

O Little Town of Bethlehem

(Third part with *F Horn* duet)

Traditional

St. Anthony chorale

(Third part with *F Horn* duet)   JOSEPH HAYDN (1732-1809)

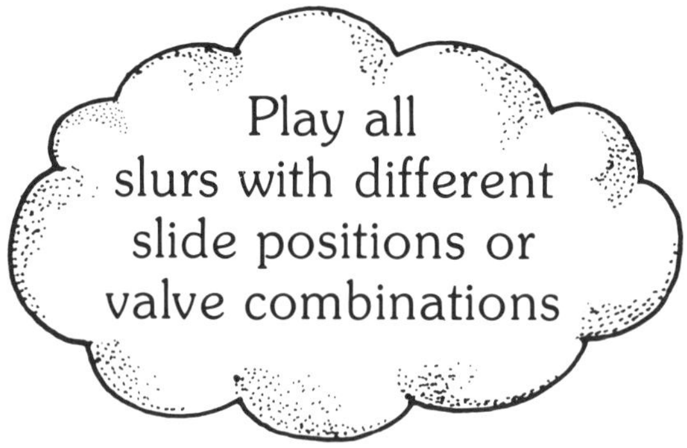

Slurs (3)

Play all slurs with different slide positions or valve combinations

■ *O Little Town of Bethlehem* and *St. Anthony chorale* for trombone duet on pages 49 & 54.

Tijuana brass

(Third part with *F Horn* duet)

I saw three ships

(Third part with *F Horn* duet)

Slurs (3) — *continued*

■ *Tijuana brass* and *I saw three ships* for
trombone duet on pages 39 & 54.

St. Anthony chorale

DUET

JOSEPH HAYDN (1732-1809)

Moderato

mf

Fine

p

p cresc.

D.C. al Fine

p subito

mf

I saw three ships

DUET

Traditional

Happily

mf

Chromatic scale

Slide positions

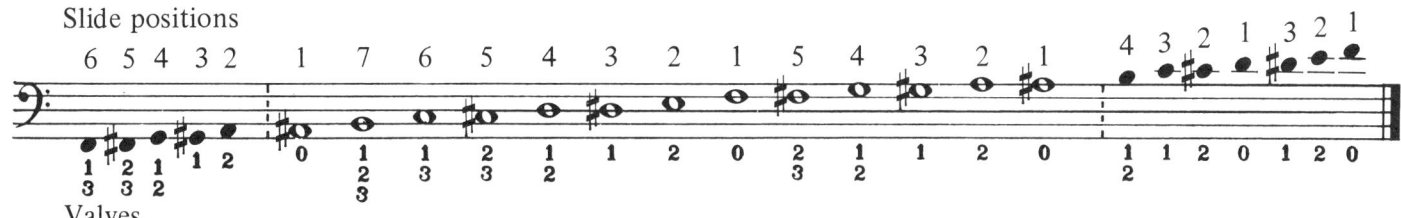

Valves

Slide positions

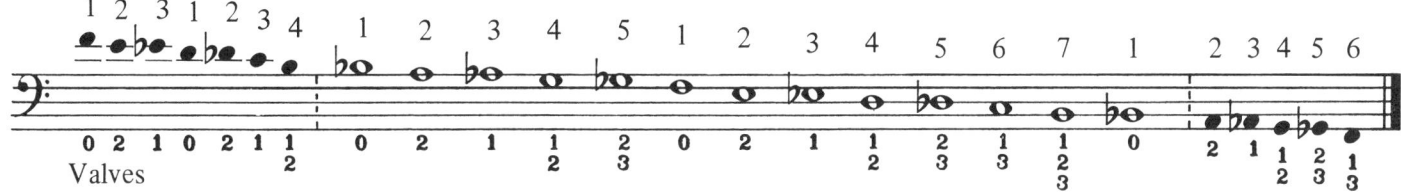

Valves

March

from *Judas Maccabaeus*
(Bass part with *Trumpet* duet)

GEORGE FRIDERIC HANDEL (1685-1759)

March

from *Judas Maccabaeus*
DUET

GEORGE FRIDERIC HANDEL (1685-1759)

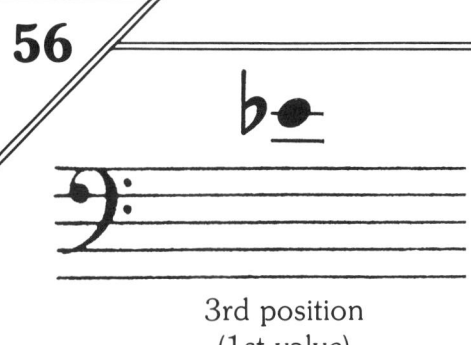

3rd position
(1st valve)

Upper E♭

Scale & arpeggio of E♭

The first noel

Traditional

Pomp and circumstance

EDWARD ELGAR (1857-1934)

The centipede's masterpiece

composed by fifteen-year old SARAH HART

Gallop

from the opera *Orpheus in the Underworld*

JACQUES OFFENBACH (1819-1880)

play by ear

Scales and arpeggios

G minor harmonic

G minor melodic

Arpeggio of G minor

C minor harmonic

C minor melodic

D major

D minor harmonic

D minor melodic

B♭ major

Arpeggio of B♭ major

A♭ major

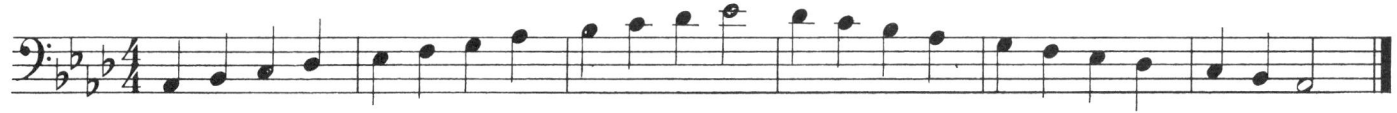

Arpeggio of A♭ major

Upper F

1st position (open)

Scale of F major

Chorale

HANS HASSLER (1564-1612)

Legato e cantabile

mp

mf

p

'Star Wars' Main Title

JOHN WILLIAMS

Allegro assai

To Coda

D. 𝄋 al Coda

CODA

D.S. al Coda means repeat the section from 𝄋 to ⊕ and then cut to the CODA section

Relaxation exercises on page 33.

Slurs (4)

March

from *Judas Maccabaeus*
(Third part with *F Horn* duet)

GEORGE FRIDERIC HANDEL (1685-1759)

■ *March* for Trombone duet on page 55.

Printed by Halstan & Co. Ltd., Amersham, Bucks., England

Glossary of musical terms

MUSICAL TERM	ABBREVIATION	MEANING IN ENGLISH
forte	f	loudly
mezzoforte	mf	(lit. half) moderately loud
piano	p	softly
mezzopiano	mp	(lit. half) moderately softly
fortissimo	ff	very loudly
pianissimo	pp	very softly
crescendo	cresc. or ◁	getting louder
diminuendo	dim. or ▷	getting quieter
ritenuto/ritardando	rit.	getting slower
a tempo		at the original speed
tempo		speed
subito	sub.	suddenly
Moderato		at a moderate speed
Allegro		merry, quick, bright
Grandioso		grandly
Con brio		with spirit
simile	sim.	Continue playing in same style
Langsam		slowly
Da Capo (Al fine)	D.C. or D.C. al Fine	Go back to the beginning (and stop at the place marked Fine)
Presto		quickly
staccato	♪ ♪ ♪	detached, ie, the opposite of Legato
tenuto	♪ ♪ ♪	Hold for full value
rallentando	rall.	gradually slowing down
Religioso		religiously
Semplice		simply
Andante		at walking pace
Maestoso		majestically
Adagio		slowly
piano-(forte)	$p(f)$	Play quietly first time, and loudly when music is repeated
Common time	C	$\frac{4}{4}$ ie four crotchets per bar
Alla Breve	¢	$\frac{2}{2}$ ie two minim beats per bar
Dal Segno	D. 𝄋 (al Coda)	Go back to the 'sign' (and then go to Coda')
Assai		very
Legato		smoothly
Cantabile		in a singing style
Et E		and
Ossia		alternative